CONTENTS

C000134481

www.skipscrosswords.co.uk

Number Lines – Adding

The + sign means we add, the = sign shows the total.

Count the animals and write the answer into the box.
Copy the answer into the CrossMaths puzzle as shown.

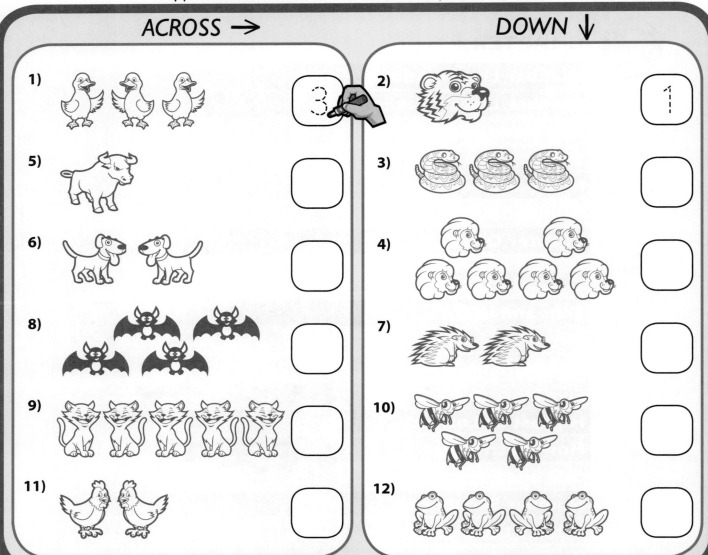

ACROSS →

1)
5)
6)
8)
9)
11)

DOWN ↓

2)
3)
4)
7)
10)
12)

Using Number Lines to Add

Hints

When adding numbers together just count forwards along the line.
The order in which you add does not matter, **3+5** is the same as **5+3**.

Step ① Start with the bigger number.
Step ② Count forward along the line.

For example: **4+3=7**

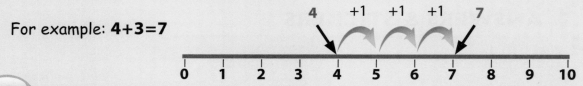

2

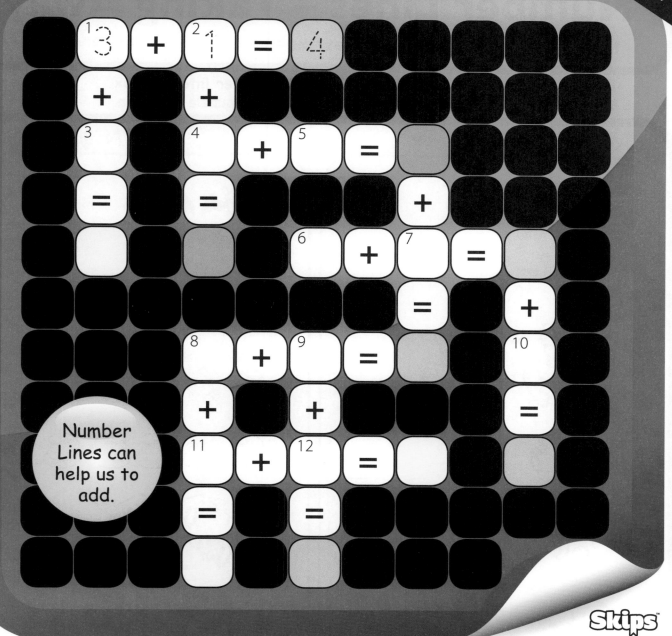

Number Lines can help us to add.

Skips

SKIPS CHALLENGE TIME

Well done! Copy the numbers from the coloured tiles in the CrossMaths to the matching coloured boxes below. Match the number name to the correct number.

Remember: boxes that are the same colour have the same number in them.

six   nine   four   seven

6

Place a SKIPS CHALLENGE sticker here

Well done! It's SKIPS sticker time.

Number Lines – Taking Away

The – sign means we take away, the = sign shows the difference.

Count the animals and write the answer into the box.
Copy the answer into the CrossMaths puzzle as shown.

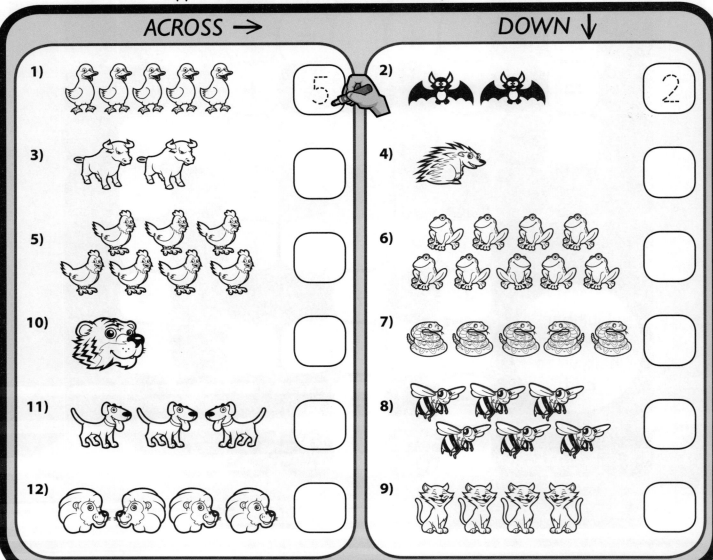

ACROSS →

1) ☐ 5

3)

5)

10)

11)

12)

DOWN ↓

2) ☐ 2

4)

6)

7)

8)

9)

Using Number Lines to Take Away

When taking away numbers just count backwards along the line.
The order in which you take away DOES matter, **5–3** is NOT the same as **3–5**.

Step ① Start with the first number.

Step ② Count backwards to the left along the line.

For example: **6–2=4**

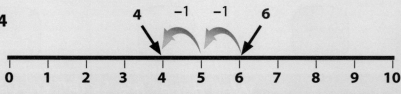

Number Lines can help us to take away.

SKIPS CHALLENGE TIME

Well done! Copy the numbers from the coloured tiles in the CrossMaths to the matching coloured boxes below. **Match the number name to the correct number.**

Remember: boxes that are the same colour have the same number in them.

 six   three   two   one

Well done! It's SKIPS sticker time.

One More or One Less

To find One More we add 1. To find One Less we take away 1.

Count the stars and answer the question. Write the answer into the box.
Copy the answer into the CrossMaths puzzle as shown.

ACROSS →

How many stars will there be if there was one more?

2) ★   total if you add 1 more → 2

4) ★★   total if you add 1 more →

7) ★★★ ★★★★   total if you add 1 more →

8) ★★ ★★★   total if you add 1 more →

11) ★★★   total if you add 1 more →

12) ★★ ★★   total if you add 1 more →

DOWN ↓

How many stars will there be if there was one less?

1) ★★★ ★★★★   total if you make 1 less → 6

3) ★★   total if you make 1 less →

5) ★★★ ★★★   total if you make 1 less →

6) ★★ ★★   total if you make 1 less →

9) ★★★   total if you make 1 less →

10) ★   total if you make 1 less →

Use the Number Line to help you *Hints*

When finding One More than a number, make one forward jump along the line.
For example: one more than 6 is 7

+1

0 1 2 3 4 5 6 7 8 9 10

$6+1=7$

When finding One Less than a number, make one jump backwards along the line.
For example: one less than 6 is 5

−1

0 1 2 3 4 5 6 7 8 9 10

$6-1=5$

6

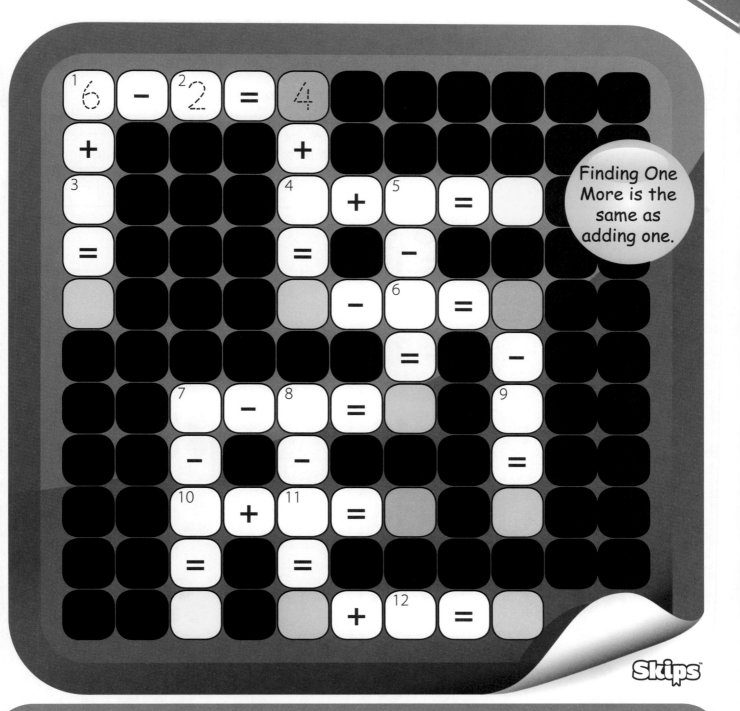

SKIPS CHALLENGE TIME

Well done! Copy the numbers from the coloured tiles in the CrossMaths to the matching coloured boxes below and then **complete the questions**.

Remember: boxes that are the same colour have the same number in them.

A.

B.

Number Bonds of 10

These are pairs of numbers that add up to ten.

Count the dots and work out how many more are needed to make ten.
Write the answer into the box. Copy the answer into the CrossMaths puzzle as shown.

ACROSS →   DOWN ↓

1) ● + [4] = 10

5) ● + [ ] = 10

6) ● + [ ] = 10

10) ● + [ ] = 10

11) ● + [ ] = 10

12) ● + [ ] = 10

2) [6] + ● = 10

3) [ ] + ● = 10

4) [ ] + ● = 10

7) [ ] + ● = 10

8) [ ] + ● = 10

9) [ ] + ● = 10

Number Bonds

9+1 gives the same answer as **1+9**. It does not matter which way around you
add the numbers. The number bonds of ten are:

| 0 and 10 | 1 and 9 | 2 and 8 | 3 and 7 | 4 and 6 | 5 and 5 |
| 10 and 0 | 9 and 1 | 8 and 2 | 7 and 3 | 6 and 4 | |

8

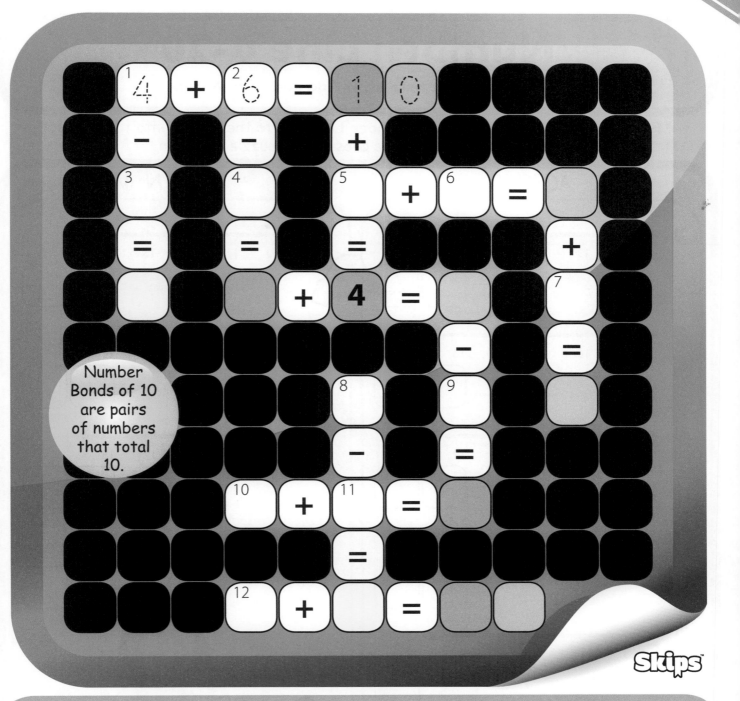

Number Bonds of 10 are pairs of numbers that total 10.

$^1 4 + {}^2 6 = 1\ 0$

SKIPS CHALLENGE TIME

Well done! Copy the numbers from the coloured tiles in the CrossMaths to the matching coloured boxes below and then complete the question.

Remember: boxes that are the same colour have the same number in them.

A. ☐ ☐ + ☐ = ☐ ☐

B. ☐ ☐ − ☐ = ☐ ☐

Place a SKIPS CHALLENGE sticker here

Well done! It's SKIPS sticker time.

www.skipscrosswords.co.uk

Number Line 0-20

Number Lines help us to Add and Take Away.

Find the missing number on the Number Line. Write the answer into the boxes.
Copy the answer into the CrossMaths puzzle as shown.

ACROSS →   ## DOWN ↓

1) 12 13 **?** 15 16   `1` `4`

2) 10 11 **?** 13 14   `1` `2`

6) 9 10 **?** 12 13

3) 16 17 **?** 19 20

7) 8 9 **?** 11 12

4) 14 15 **?** 17 18

8) 14 15 **?** 17 18

5) 8 9 **?** 11 12

9) 3 4 **?** 6 7

10) 13 14 **?** 16 17

Number Line to 20
Use the Number Line to help you.

+1

0 1 2 3 4 5 6 7 8 9 10 11 12 13 14 15 16 17 18 19 20

−1

Hints

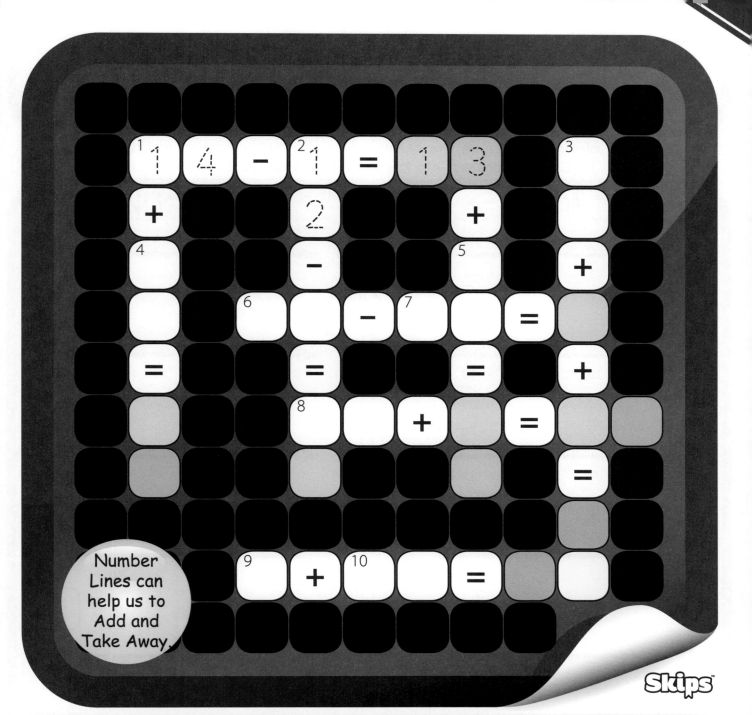

Number Lines can help us to Add and Take Away.

$$14 - 1 = 13$$

$$12$$

Skips

Number Line 0-30

Number Lines help us to Add and Take Away.

Find the missing number on the Number Line. Write the answer into the boxes.
Copy the answer into the CrossMaths puzzle as shown.

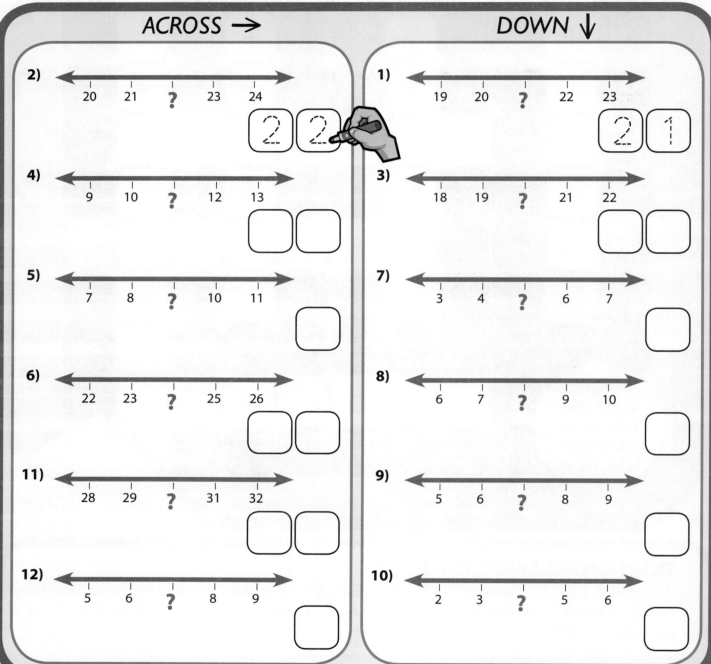

ACROSS →

2) 20 21 ? 23 24   [2] [2]

4) 9 10 ? 12 13   [ ] [ ]

5) 7 8 ? 10 11   [ ]

6) 22 23 ? 25 26   [ ] [ ]

11) 28 29 ? 31 32   [ ] [ ]

12) 5 6 ? 8 9   [ ]

DOWN ↓

1) 19 20 ? 22 23   [2] [1]

3) 18 19 ? 21 22   [ ] [ ]

7) 3 4 ? 6 7   [ ]

8) 6 7 ? 9 10   [ ]

9) 5 6 ? 8 9   [ ]

10) 2 3 ? 5 6   [ ]

Number Line to 30

Use the Number Line to help you.

0 2 4 6 8 10 12 14 16 18 20 22 24 26 28 30
 1 3 5 7 9 11 13 15 17 19 21 23 25 27 29

Hints

12

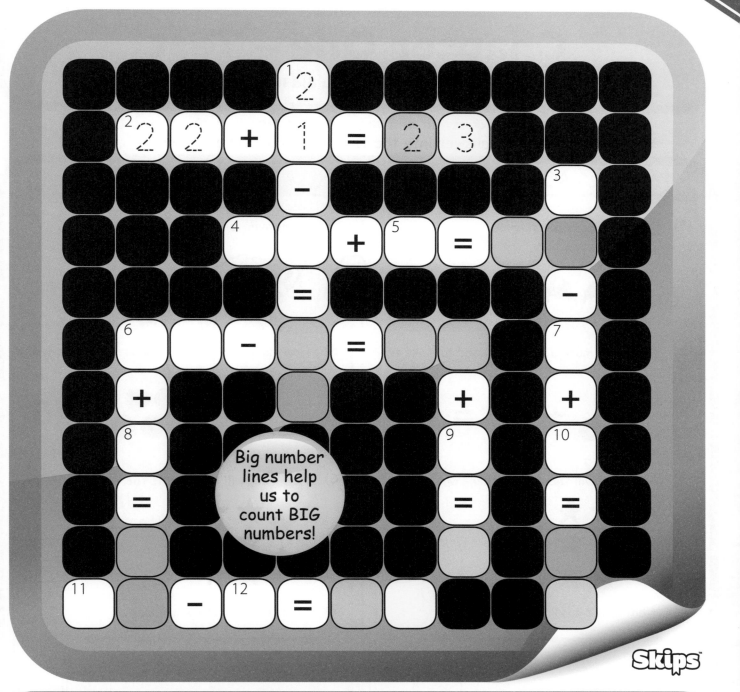

Big number lines help us to count BIG numbers!

SKIPS CHALLENGE TIME

Well done! Copy the numbers from the coloured tiles in the CrossMaths to the matching coloured boxes below and then match the number name to the correct number.

Remember: boxes that are the same colour have the same number in them.

 twenty

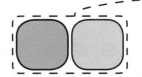 twenty three

thirty

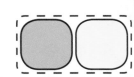 nineteen

Place a SKIPS CHALLENGE sticker here

Well done! It's SKIPS sticker time.

13

www.skipscrosswords.co.uk

Chapter One – Test

Can you remember what you did in this chapter?

Answer each question and write the answer into the boxes.
Copy the answer into the CrossMaths puzzle as shown.

ACROSS →

1) How many bats are there?

 3

2) How many more dots are needed to make ten?

 $+ \boxed{} = 10$

3) How many will there be if there was one more?

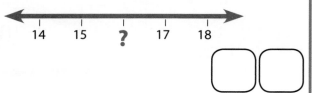 ☐☐

8) What is the missing number?

14   15   **?**   17   18

☐☐

11) What is the missing number?

27   28   **?**   30   31

☐☐

12) How many will there be if there was one more?

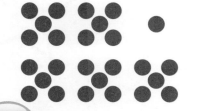 ☐☐

DOWN ↓

4) How many bees are there?

 7

5) How many more dots are needed to make ten?

$\boxed{} +$  $= 10$

6) How many will there be if there was one less?

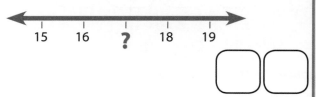 ☐

7) What is the missing number?

15   16   **?**   18   19

☐☐

9) What is the missing number?

20   21   **?**   23   24

☐☐

10) How many will there be if there was one less?

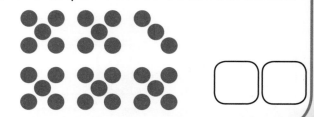 ☐☐

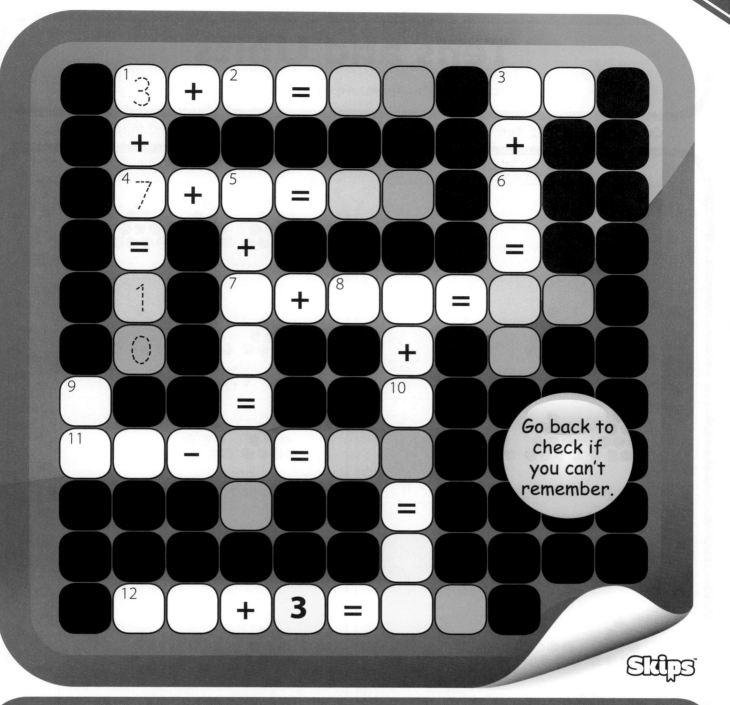

Go back to check if you can't remember.

Skips

SKIPS CHALLENGE TIME

Well done! Copy the numbers from the coloured tiles in the CrossMaths to the matching coloured boxes below then answer the question below.

Remember: boxes that are the same colour have the same number in them.

Copy out the largest number.

Great! Show your teacher how well you've done.

15

Tens and Units

Two digit numbers are made up from Tens and Units.

Count the lots of ten and the units. Copy the answer into the CrossMaths puzzle.

ACROSS → ## DOWN ↓

1)
_1_ lot of ten + _0_ units = [1][0]

2)
___ lots of ten + ___ units = [ ][ ]

3)
_3_ lots of ten + _0_ units = [3][0]

4)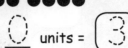
___ lots of ten + ___ units = [ ][ ]

5)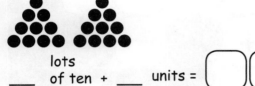
___ lots of ten + ___ units = [ ][ ]

6)
___ lots of ten + ___ units = [ ][ ]

7)
___ lot of ten + ___ units = [ ][ ]

8)
___ lot of ten + ___ units = [ ][ ]

9)
___ lot of ten + ___ units = [ ][ ]

10)
___ lot of ten + ___ unit = [ ][ ]

12)
___ lot of ten + ___ units = [ ][ ]

11)
___ lots of ten + ___ units = [ ][ ]

Tens and Units

If we group things in sets of TENS and UNITS it is easier to understand bigger numbers. For example:

two   five
tens units

_2_ lots of ten + _5_ units = **25**

Hints

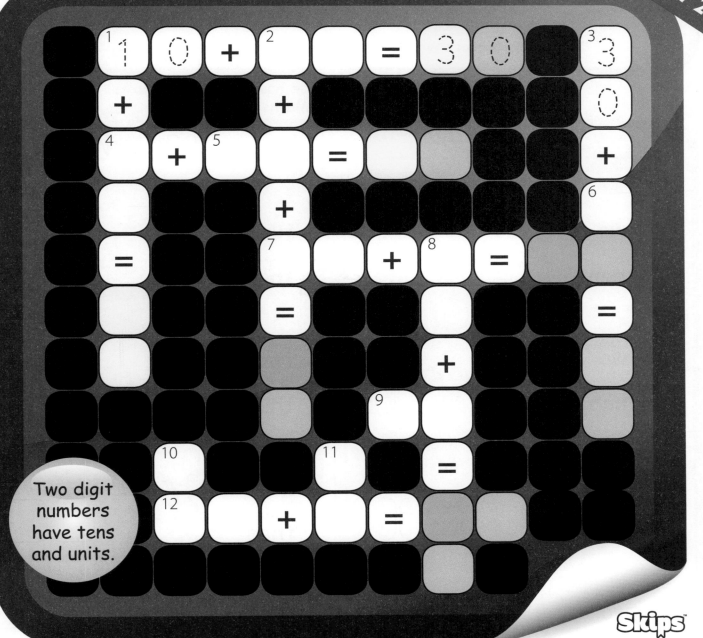

Two digit numbers have tens and units.

Skips

SKIPS CHALLENGE TIME

Well done! Copy the numbers from the coloured tiles in the CrossMaths to the matching coloured boxes below then **answer the questions below.**

Remember: boxes that are the same colour have the same number in them.

A. Copy out the smallest number:

B. Copy out the largest number:

Place a SKIPS CHALLENGE sticker here

Well done! It's SKIPS sticker time.

www.skipscrosswords.co.uk

Two More or Two Less

To find Two More we add 2. To find Two Less we take away 2.

Answer each question and write the answer into the boxes.
Copy the answer into the CrossMaths puzzle as shown.

ACROSS →

1) two more than 10 → `1` `2`

4) two more than 18 → ☐ ☐

8) two more than 20 → ☐ ☐

9) two more than 28 → ☐ ☐

10) two more than 29 → ☐ ☐

12) two more than 24 → ☐ ☐

DOWN ↓

2) two less than 22 → `2` `0`

3) two less than 12 → ☐ ☐

5) two less than 26 → ☐ ☐

6) two less than 20 → ☐ ☐

7) two less than 30 → ☐ ☐

11) two less than 29 → ☐ ☐

18

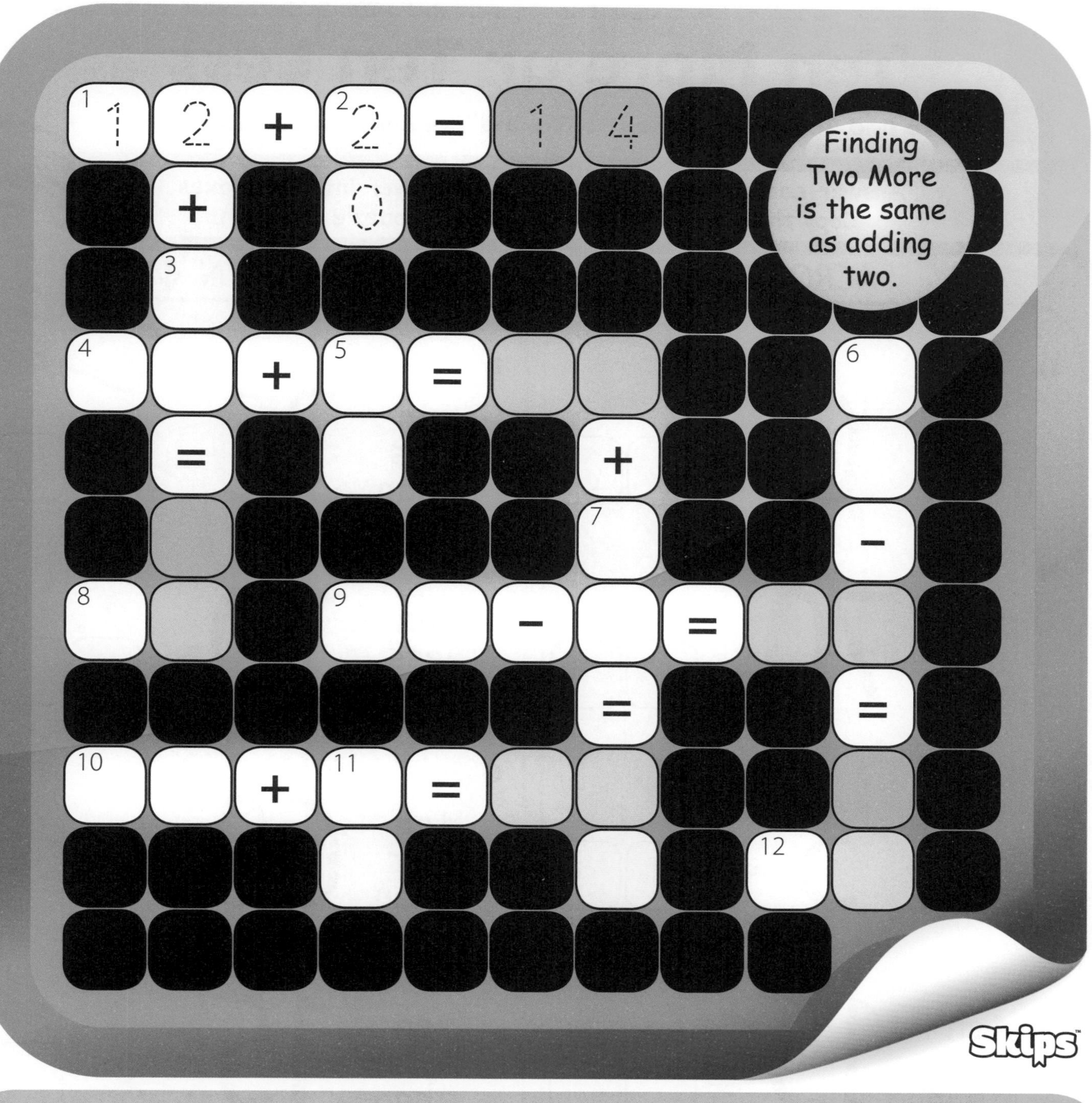
1
12 + 2
2
= 14
+
0
3
4
+
5
=
6
=
+
7
–
8
9
–
=
=
=
10
+
11
=
12
Finding Two More is the same as adding two.

SKIPS CHALLENGE TIME

Well done! Copy the numbers from the coloured tiles in the CrossMaths to the matching coloured boxes below then answer the questions below.

Remember: boxes that are the same colour have the same number in them.

A. Copy out the largest number:

B. Copy out the smallest number:

Place a SKIPS CHALLENGE sticker here

Well done! It's SKIPS sticker time.

Ten More or Ten Less

To find Ten More we add 10. To find Ten Less we take away 10.

Answer each question and write the answer into the boxes.
Copy the answer into the CrossMaths puzzle as shown.

ACROSS →   **DOWN ↓**

1) ten more than 0 → [1][0]

2) ten less than 30 → [2][0]

3) ten more than 70 → [ ][ ]

4) ten less than 20 → [ ][ ]

5) ten more than 5 → [ ][ ]

6) ten less than 60 → [ ][ ]

7) ten more than 15 → [ ][ ]

8) ten less than 15 → [ ]

9) ten more than 80 → [ ][ ]

10) ten less than 50 → [ ][ ]

11) ten more than 90 → [ ][ ][ ]

12) ten less than 100 → [ ][ ][ ]

20

Ten More – just add ten. Simple!

Skips

SKIPS CHALLENGE TIME

Well done! Copy the numbers from the coloured tiles in the CrossMaths to the matching coloured boxes below then answer the questions below.

Remember: boxes that are the same colour have the same number in them.

A. Copy out the largest number:

B. Copy out the smallest number:

Place a SKIPS CHALLENGE sticker here

Five More or Five Less

To find Five More we add 5. To find Five Less we take away 5.

Answer each question and write the answer into the boxes.
Copy the answer into the CrossMaths puzzle as shown.

ACROSS →   ## DOWN ↓

1) five more than **10** → [1][5]

2) five less than **55** → [5][0]

5) five more than **40** → [ ][ ]

3) five less than **20** → [ ][ ]

7) five more than **45** → [ ][ ]

4) five less than **25** → [ ][ ]

8) five more than **0** → [ ]

6) five less than **60** → [ ][ ]

9) five more than **4** → [ ]

10) five less than **95** → [ ][ ]

12) five more than **95** → [ ][ ][ ]

11) five less than **10** → [ ]

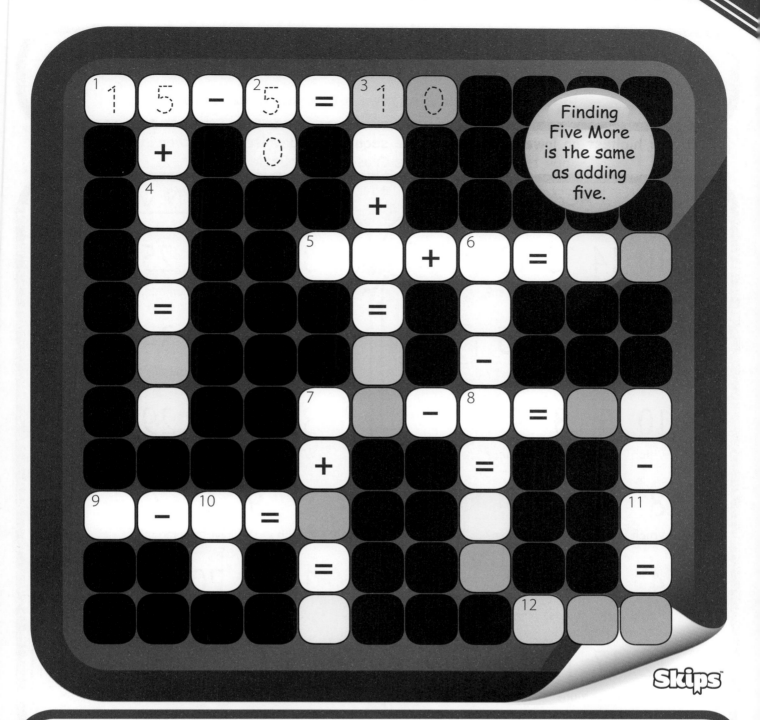

Skips

SKIPS CHALLENGE TIME

Well done! Copy the numbers from the coloured tiles in the CrossMaths to the matching coloured boxes below and then **match the number name to the correct number**.

Remember: boxes that are the same colour have the same number in them.

twenty five   one hundred   fifty five   fourteen

Take your book to school and ask your teacher to put a **WELL DONE SKIP!** sticker here, and there's another sticker for you.

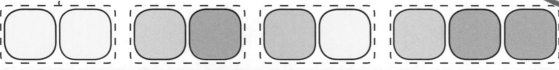

Great! Now show your teacher how well you've done.

Highest or Lowest?

Finding the highest or lowest in a set of numbers.

Find the highest or lowest number in the sequence and write the answer into the boxes.
Copy the answer into the CrossMaths puzzle as shown.

ACROSS →

1) 10 14 13 12 $\boxed{1}\boxed{4}$
Which is the highest number?

3) 20 10 25 15 ☐☐
Which is the highest number?

4) 10 5 8 9 ☐☐
Which is the highest number?

9) 8 9 6 7 ☐
Which is the highest number?

11) 4 8 6 2 ☐
Which is the highest number?

12) 12 17 15 14 ☐☐
Which is the highest number?

DOWN ↓

2) 35 30 20 25 $\boxed{2}\boxed{0}$
Which is the lowest number?

5) 36 32 35 34 ☐☐
Which is the lowest number?

6) 30 31 35 29 ☐☐
Which is the lowest number?

7) 5 9 6 7 ☐
Which is the lowest number?

8) 17 18 20 16 ☐☐
Which is the lowest number?

10) 12 10 9 7 ☐
Which is the lowest number?

Ordering Numbers

Hints

When we put two digit numbers in order, we need to look first at the TENS and then the UNITS digits. You can use a number line to help.

For example: **34** is larger than **16**, because there are more tens, **3** is more than **1**.

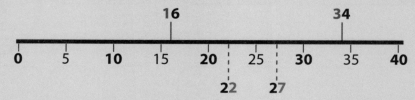

If the tens are the same, we look at the units digit, **27** is larger than **22**, because there are more units, **7** is more than **2**.

24

For more SKIPS titles visit our website.

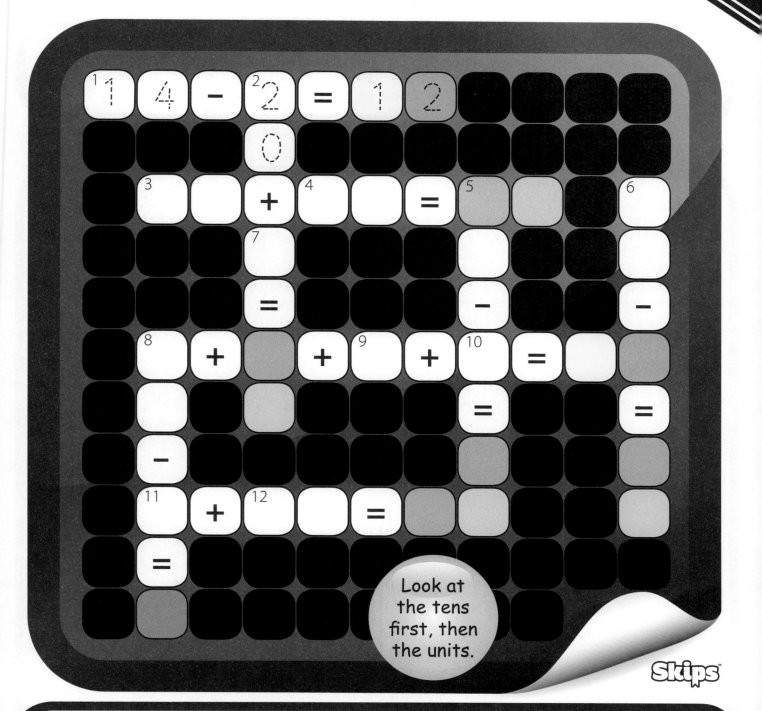

SKIPS CHALLENGE TIME

Well done! Copy the numbers from the coloured tiles in the CrossMaths to the matching coloured boxes below and then **answer the questions**.

Remember: boxes that are the same colour have the same number in them.

A.

B.

Place a SKIPS
CHALLENGE
sticker
here

Well done! It's SKIPS sticker time.

25

www.skipscrosswords.co.uk

How Much Money?

We need to know the value of coins when using money.

Add up the values on the coins. Write the answer in the boxes.
Copy the answer into the CrossMaths puzzle as shown.

ACROSS →   DOWN ↓

2)   `1` `5`

1)   `2` `5`

4)  [ ] [ ]

3)   [ ] [ ]

5)  [ ]

7) [ ]

6)    [ ] [ ]

8)  [ ]

11)       [ ] [ ]

9) [ ]

12)     [ ]

10)   [ ]

British Coins

1p   one pence
2p  two pence
5p   five pence
10p  ten pence
20p   twenty pence

For more SKIPS titles visit our website.

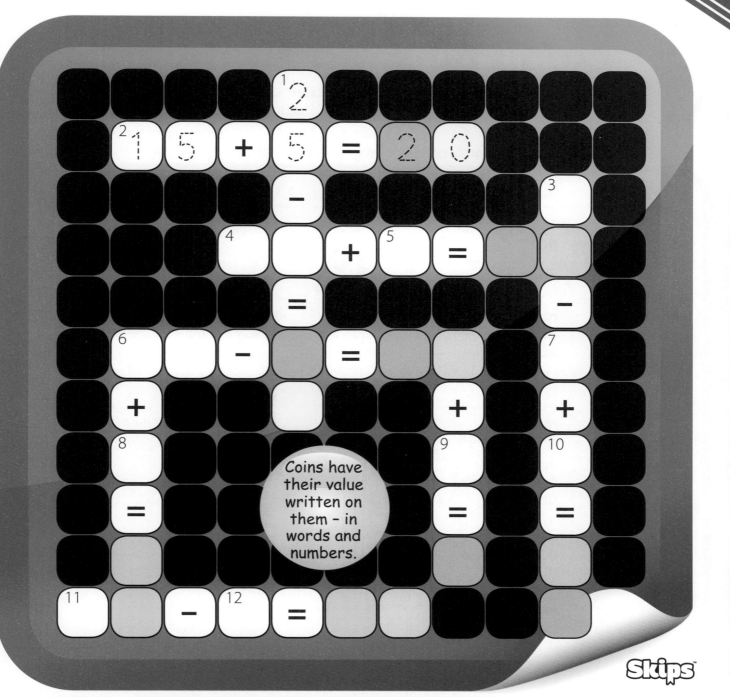

Coins have their value written on them – in words and numbers.

SKIPS CHALLENGE TIME

Well done! Copy the numbers from the coloured tiles in the CrossMaths to the matching coloured boxes below and then **match the number name to the correct number**.

Remember: boxes that are the same colour have the same number in them.

| twenty | fifty | seventy | ten |

Well done! It's SKIPS sticker time.

Odd and Even Numbers

All whole numbers are either Odd or Even.

Find out the next odd or even number and write the answer into the boxes.
Copy the answer into the CrossMaths puzzle as shown.

ACROSS →

1) 12 next even number → [1][4]

3) 11 next odd number → [ ][ ]

4) 8 next even number → [ ][ ]

10) 31 next odd number → [ ][ ]

11) 21 next odd number → [ ][ ]

12) 28 next even number → [ ][ ]

13) 18 next even number → [ ][ ]

DOWN ↓

2) 8 next even number → [1][0]

5) 19 next odd number → [ ][ ]

6) 11 next odd number → [ ][ ]

7) 24 next even number → [ ][ ]

8) 9 next odd number → [ ][ ]

9) 18 next even number → [ ][ ]

Odd and Even Numbers

Hints

ODD numbers are those which end in 1, 3, 5, 7 or 9.
EVEN numbers end in 2, 4, 6, 8 or 0.
On a number line, ODD and EVEN numbers take it in turns.

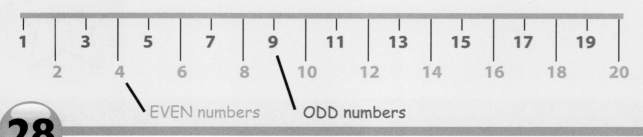

1 3 5 7 9 11 13 15 17 19
2 4 6 8 10 12 14 16 18 20

EVEN numbers   ODD numbers

For more SKIPS titles visit our website.

The CrossMaths grid contains:

$$14 - 1 = 13$$

with $+$ and 0 below in the second column.

Speech bubble: **Even numbers end in 2, 4, 6, 8 or 0.**

Grid clues numbered 1–13 with operators: $+$, $=$, $+$, $=$, $=$, $-$, $-$, $-$, $=$, $=$, $+$

SKIPS CHALLENGE TIME

Well done! Copy the numbers from the coloured tiles in the CrossMaths to the matching coloured boxes below then answer the questions below.

Remember: boxes that are the same colour have the same number in them.

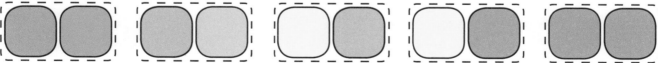

A. Find the smallest ODD number:

B. Find the largest ODD number:

Place a SKIPS CHALLENGE sticker here

Well done! It's SKIPS sticker time.

Number Sequences

A sequence is a pattern of numbers.

Complete the **number sequences** and write the answer into the boxes.
Copy the answer into the CrossMaths puzzle as shown.

ACROSS →

DOWN ↓

1) 16 18 20 22 ②④

2) 2 4 6 8 ☐☐

6) 6 9 12 15 ☐☐

8) 5 ☐☐ 15 20 25

9) 8 11 14 17 ☐☐

11) 14 17 ☐☐ 23 26

3) 10 12 14 16 ①⑧

4) 16 18 20 ☐☐ 24

5) 17 20 23 26 ☐☐

7) 5 10 15 ☐☐ 25

10) 5 7 9 ☐☐ 13

Number Sequences or Number Patterns

Hints

You can find the pattern in a sequence of numbers by looking at the difference between the numbers.

For example: look at the sequence **12 14 16 18**

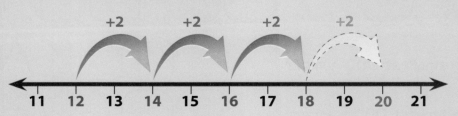

The difference between each number is **2** and from this pattern we can then work out that the next number in the sequence will be **20**.

30

Find the difference to find the pattern.

Skips

SKIPS CHALLENGE TIME

Well done! Copy the numbers from the coloured tiles in the CrossMaths to the matching coloured boxes below and then **complete the sequence**.

Remember: boxes that are the same colour have the same number in them.

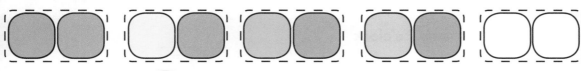

Place a SKIPS CHALLENGE sticker here

Well done! It's SKIPS sticker time.

What's the Time?

Telling the time using two types of clock.

What's the time shown on each clock? Write the answer into the boxes.
Copy the answer into the CrossMaths puzzle as shown.

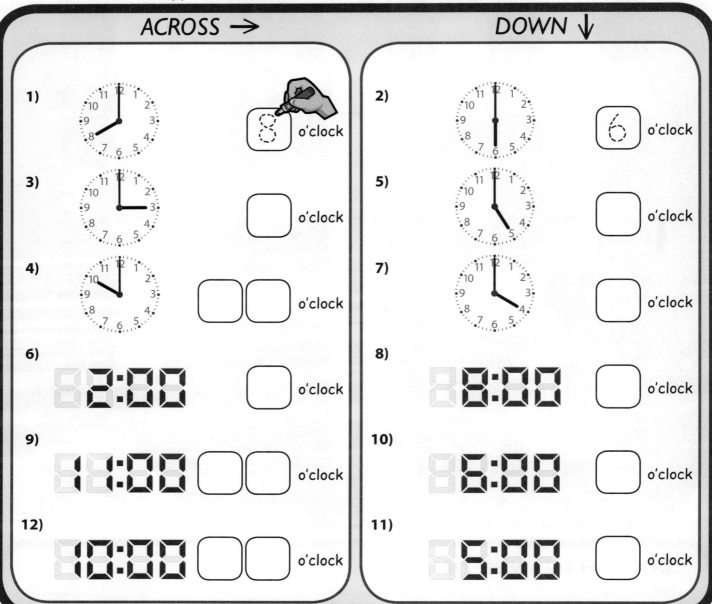

ACROSS →

DOWN ↓

1) [8] o'clock

2) [6] o'clock

3) [ ] o'clock

5) [ ] o'clock

4) [ ][ ] o'clock

7) [ ] o'clock

6) 2:00 [ ] o'clock

8) 8:00 [ ] o'clock

9) 11:00 [ ][ ] o'clock

10) 6:00 [ ] o'clock

12) 10:00 [ ][ ] o'clock

11) 5:00 [ ] o'clock

Two Types of Clockface

Both clocks are showing the time as **2** o'clock.

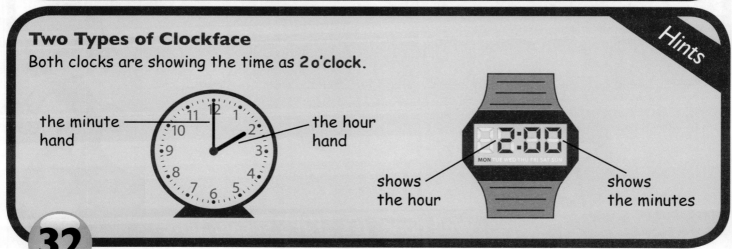

the minute hand

the hour hand

shows the hour

shows the minutes

Hints

32

There are 60 minutes in an hour.

Skips

SKIPS CHALLENGE TIME

Well done! Copy the numbers from the coloured tiles in the CrossMaths to the matching coloured boxes and then **complete the sentences.**

A. ⬜⬜ : ⬜⬜ and ⬜⬜ : ⬜⬜

There are ⬜⬜ minutes between these two times.

B. ⬜⬜ : ⬜⬜ and ⬜⬜ : ⬜⬜

There are ⬜⬜ minutes between these two times.

Place a SKIPS CHALLENGE sticker here

Well done! It's SKIPS sticker time.

Chapter Two – Test

Can you remember what you did in this chapter?

Answer each question and write the answer into the boxes.
Copy the answer into the CrossMaths puzzle as shown.

ACROSS →

1)

__3__ lots of ten + __2__ units = ⌈3⌉⌈2⌉

2)

two more than **8** → ☐☐

5)

five more than **5** → ☐☐

7)

ten more than **17** → ☐☐

11)

18 next even number → ☐☐

12) How much money is there altogether?

☐☐

DOWN ↓

3)

__2__ lots of ten + __6__ units = ⌈2⌉⌈6⌉

4)

two less than **19** → ☐☐

6)

five less than **30** → ☐☐

8)

ten less than **15** → ☐

9)

5 next odd number → ☐

10) How much money is there altogether?

☐☐

For more SKIPS titles visit our website.

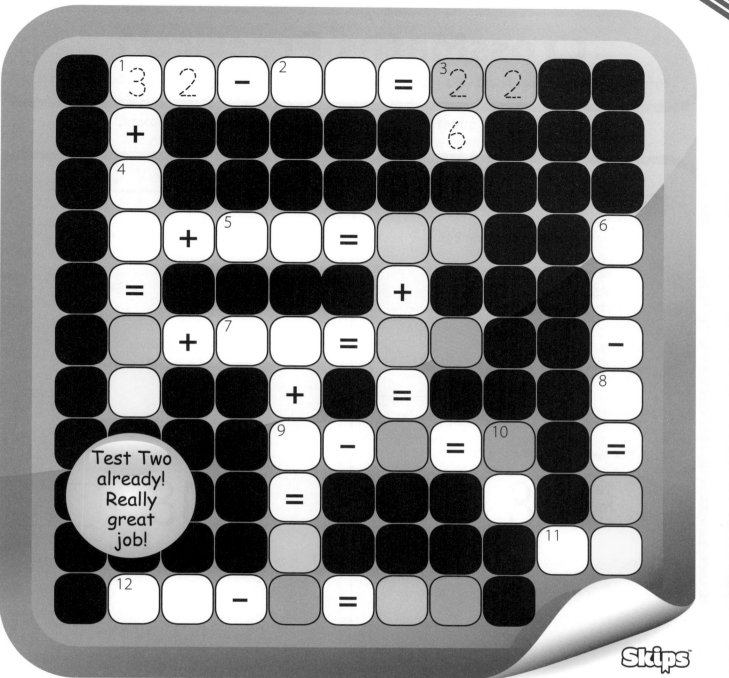

SKIPS CHALLENGE TIME

Well done! Copy the numbers from the coloured tiles in the CrossMaths to the matching coloured boxes below then answer the question below.

Remember: boxes that are the same colour have the same number in them.

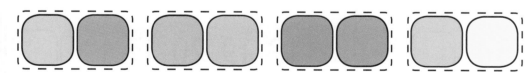

Find the EVEN number:

Take your book to school and ask your teacher to put a

WELL DONE SKIP!

sticker here, and there's another sticker for you.

Great! Show your teacher how well you've done.

CrossMaths Practice 1

Practice makes perfect! To get really good at something you need to practise.

Answer each question and write the answer into the boxes.
Copy the answer into the CrossMaths puzzle as shown.

ACROSS → DOWN ↓

1) What number is ten less than 24?

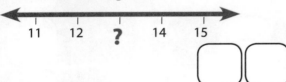

2) What number is two more than 8?

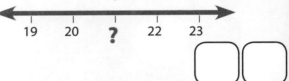

3) What is the missing number?

11 12 **?** 14 15

5) What is the missing number?

19 20 **?** 22 23

4) What number is two more than 8?

two more than **8** →

6) What number is five less than 18?

five less than **18** →

10) How much money is there altogether?

7) How much money is there altogether?

11) What is the next odd number after 21?

21 next odd number →

8) What is the next odd number after 9?

9 next odd number →

12) Which is the lowest number?

36 32 30 34

9) Which is the highest number?

12 19 20 17

13) What is the missing number in the sequence?

16 18 ☐ ☐ 22 24

Chapter 3

Great work, keep it up!

SKIPS CHALLENGE TIME

Well done! Copy the numbers from the coloured tiles in the CrossMaths to the matching coloured boxes below and then **answer the question**.

Remember: boxes that are the same colour have the same number in them.

You have p. You buy a drink for ☐☐p.

How much money do you have left? ☐☐p.

Place a SKIPS CHALLENGE sticker here

CrossMaths Practice 2

Practice makes perfect! **To get really good at something you need to practise.**

Answer each question and write the answer into the boxes.
Copy the answer into the CrossMaths puzzle as shown.

ACROSS →

1) What is the difference between 10 and 7?

2) What is the sum of 4 and 3?

3) What time is shown on the clock?

☐ ☐ o'clock

8) What is 4 less than 20?

15   16   17   18   19   20

☐ ☐

11) How much money is there altogether?

☐ ☐

12) Add the numbers and complete the sum.

$$14 + 13 = \boxed{}\boxed{}$$

DOWN ↓

4) What is the difference between 10 and 3?

5) What is the total of one and two?

☐

6) What time is shown on the clock?

☐ o'clock

7) What is 5 less than 22?

17   18   19   20   21   22

☐ ☐

9) How much money is there altogether?

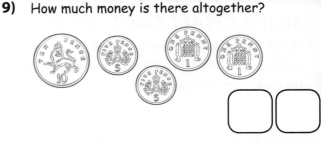

☐ ☐

10) Add the numbers and complete the sum.

$$18 + 9 = \boxed{}\boxed{}$$

38

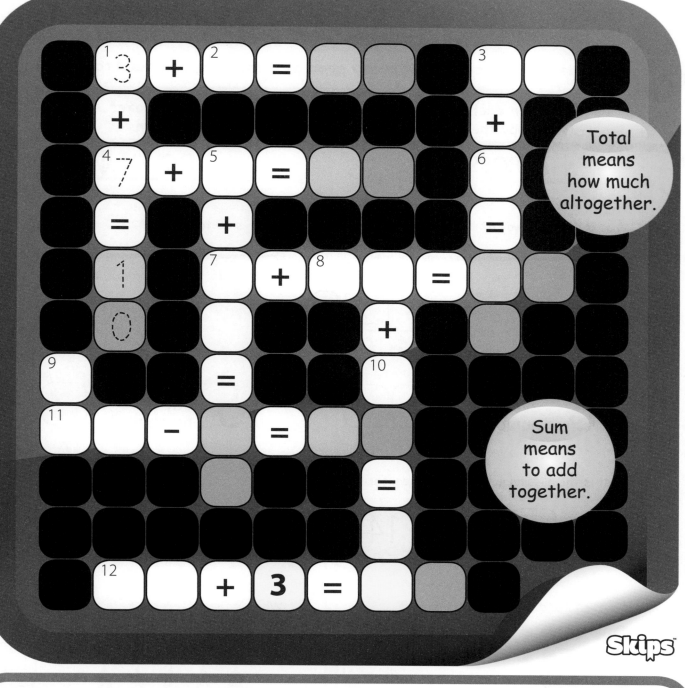

Total means how much altogether.

Sum means to add together.

Skips

SKIPS CHALLENGE TIME

Well done! Copy the numbers from the coloured tiles in the CrossMaths to the matching coloured boxes below and then **complete the sentences**.

Remember: boxes that are the same colour have the same number in them.

A. What is the difference between ▢▢ and ▢▢ ? ▢

B. What is the number that comes between

▢▢ and ▢▢ ? ▢▢

Take your book to school and ask your teacher to put a **WELL DONE SKIP!** sticker here, and there's another sticker for you.

Now show your teacher how well you've done.

CrossMaths Practice 3

Practice makes perfect! **To get really good at something you need to practise.**

Answer each question and write the answer into the boxes.
Copy the answer into the CrossMaths puzzle as shown.

ACROSS →

1) What is 40 take away 8?

32 33 34 35 36 37 38 39 40

[3] [2]

2) What is the next even number after 8?

8 next even number → ☐☐

5) What is the missing number in the sequence?

6 8 ☐ ☐ 12 14

7) What is 17 add ten?

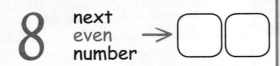

☐☐

11) Rishi has 30p in his pocket. If he spends 10p, how much does he have left?

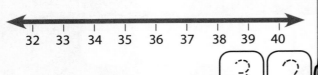

☐☐

12) What is the missing number?

26 27 ? 29 30

☐☐

DOWN ↓

3) What is 30 take away 4?

25 26 27 28 29 30

[2] [6]

4) What is the next odd number after 15?

15 next odd number → ☐☐

6) What is the missing number in the sequence?

20 ☐ ☐ 30 35 40

8) What is the difference between ten and 5?

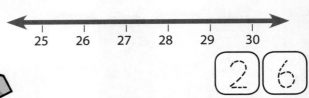

☐

9) Nicole and Sacha play a game. Nicole scores 17 points, Sacha scores 10 points. How many more points does Nicole score than Sacha?

Nicole |||| |||| |||| ||
Sacha |||| ||||

☐

10) What is the missing number?

38 39 ? 41 42

☐☐

For more SKIPS titles visit our website.

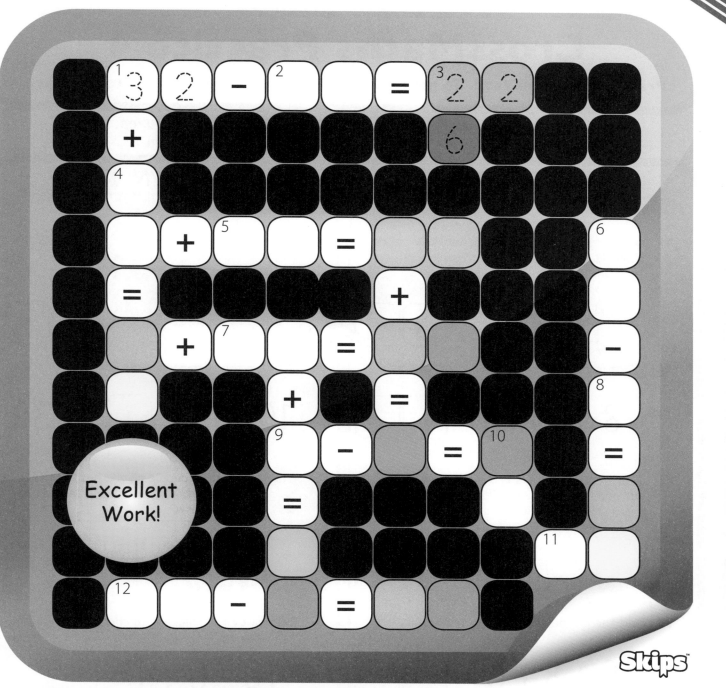

Excellent Work!

SKIPS CHALLENGE TIME

Well done! Copy the numbers from the coloured tiles in the CrossMaths to the matching coloured boxes below then complete the sequence.

Remember: boxes that are the same colour have the same number in them.

Place a SKIPS CHALLENGE sticker here

Well done! It's SKIPS sticker time.

www.skipscrosswords.co.uk

CrossMaths Practice 4

Practice makes perfect! To get really good at something you need to practise.

Answer each question and write the answer into the boxes.
Copy the answer into the CrossMaths puzzle as shown.

ACROSS →

1) Dylan is 12 years old. His father is 20 years older. How old is Dylan's Father?

4) What is the missing number in the sequence?

8 11 14 17 ☐☐

8) There are 32 sweets in a jar. 5 sweets are red and 5 sweets are yellow. The rest are green. How many sweets are green?

 ☐☐

9) Add the numbers and complete the sum.

$20+8+6=$ ☐☐

10) How much money is there altogether?

 ☐☐

12) What is the next even number after 16?

16 next even number → ☐☐

DOWN ↓

2) Lisa wants to buy one banana. She has 20p. How much more money does she need?

 2 5

3) What is the missing number in the sequence?

10 15 ☐☐ 25 30

5) There are thirty people on the bus. At the next stop one gets off. How many people are left on the bus now?

 ☐☐

6) Take away the numbers to complete the sum.

$40-6-4=$ ☐☐

7) How much money is there altogether?

 ☐☐

11) What is the next odd number after 25?

25 next odd number → ☐☐

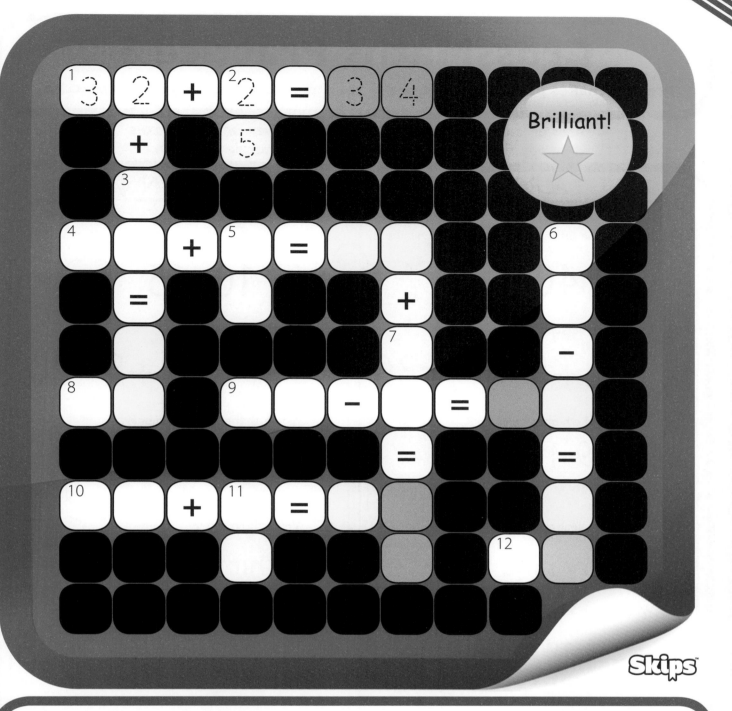

Brilliant!

Skips

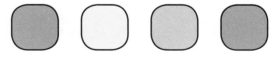
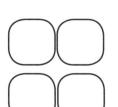
www.skipscrosswords.co.uk

CrossMaths Practice 5

Practice makes perfect! **To get really good at something you need to practise.**

Answer each question and write the answer into the boxes.
Copy the answer into the CrossMaths puzzle as shown.

ACROSS →

1) What is the difference between the numbers?

30 40 | 1 | 0 |

2) Complete the sum.

$$10 + \boxed{}\boxed{} = 30$$

5) Which is the highest number?

23 19 17 27 25 | | |

7) Write the number

forty nine | | |

9) What is ten less than twenty seven?

ten less than twenty seven | | |

12) Complete the statement.

18 is one less than | | |

DOWN ↓

3) What is the total of the numbers?

5 10 15 | 3 | 0 |

4) Complete the sum.

$$\boxed{}\boxed{} + 5 = 20$$

6) Which is the lowest number?

29 20 43 33 35 | | |

8) Write the number

thirteen | | |

10) What is five less than sixteen?

five less than sixteen | | |

11) Complete the statement.

20 is two less than | | |

Well Done Skip!

You're now ready to move up to the next SKIPS book.

For more SKIPS titles visit our website.

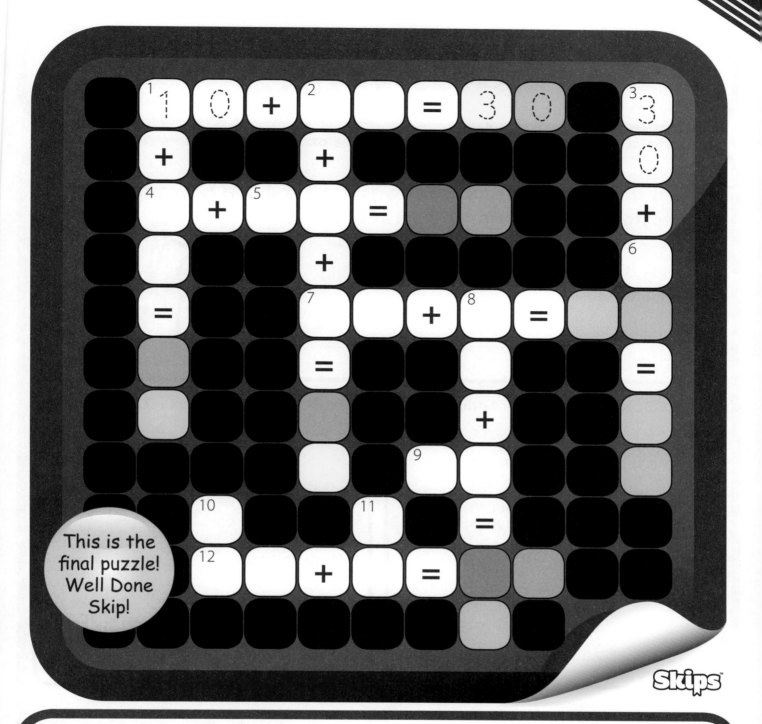

$$10 + \square = 30 \qquad 3$$

SKIPS CHALLENGE TIME

Well done! Copy the numbers from the coloured tiles in the CrossMaths to the matching coloured boxes below and then **complete the sentence**.

Remember: boxes that are the same colour have the same number in them.

A cube has ☐ faces, ☐☐ edges and ☐ corners.

Take your book to school and ask your teacher to put a **WELL DONE SKIP!** sticker here, and there's another sticker for you.

Great work! Now show your teacher how well you've done.

45

www.skipscrosswords.co.uk

ANSWERS

Well done! Now check your answers and see how many questions you answered correctly.

Good luck!

Page 2-3 Number Lines – Adding

ACROSS		DOWN	
1)	3	2)	1
5)	1	3)	3
6)	2	4)	6
8)	4	7)	2
9)	5	10)	5
11)	2	12)	4

SKIPS CHALLENGE

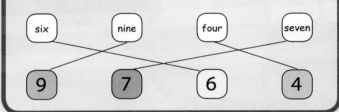

Page 4-5 Number Lines – Taking Away

ACROSS		DOWN	
1)	5	2)	2
3)	2	4)	1
5)	7	6)	9
10)	1	7)	5
11)	3	8)	6
12)	4	9)	4

SKIPS CHALLENGE

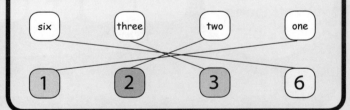

Page 6-7 One More or One Less

ACROSS		DOWN	
2)	2	1)	6
4)	3	3)	1
7)	8	5)	5
8)	6	6)	3
11)	4	9)	2
12)	5	10)	0

SKIPS CHALLENGE

A. 4 – 2 = 2

B. 8 – 7 = 1

Page 8-9 Number Bonds of 10

ACROSS		DOWN	
1)	4	2)	6
5)	3	3)	1
6)	5	4)	2
10)	4	7)	0
11)	0	8)	3
12)	7	9)	4

SKIPS CHALLENGE

A. 1 0 + 4 = 1 4

B. 1 4 – 3 = 1 1

Page 10-11 Number Line 0-20

ACROSS		DOWN	
1)	14	2)	12
6)	11	3)	18
7)	10	4)	16
8)	16	5)	10
9)	5		
10)	15		

SKIPS CHALLENGE

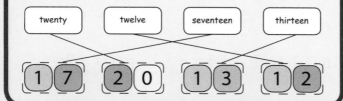

Page 12-13 Number Line 0-30

ACROSS		DOWN	
2)	22	1)	21
4)	11	3)	20
5)	9	7)	5
6)	24	8)	8
11)	30	9)	7
12)	7	10)	4

SKIPS CHALLENGE

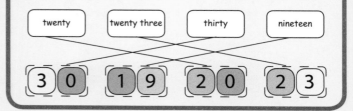

Page 14-15 Chapter One – Test

ACROSS		DOWN	
1)	3	4)	7
2)	7	5)	3
3)	11	6)	9
8)	16	7)	17
11)	29	9)	22
12)	27	10)	27

SKIPS CHALLENGE

Copy out the largest number. 2 7

Page 16-17 Tens and Units

ACROSS		DOWN	
1)	10	3)	30
2)	20	4)	32
5)	27	6)	20
7)	19	8)	13
9)	17	10)	11
12)	18	11)	22

SKIPS CHALLENGE

2 3   3 0   1 2   3 2

A. Copy out the smallest number: 1 2

B. Copy out the largest number: 3 2

Page 18-19 Two More or Two Less

ACROSS		DOWN	
1)	12	2)	20
4)	20	3)	10
8)	22	5)	24
9)	30	6)	18
10)	31	7)	28
12)	26	11)	27

SKIPS CHALLENGE

1 4   3 6   2 0   3 4

A. Copy out the largest number: 3 6

B. Copy out the smallest number: 1 4

Page 20-21 Ten More or Ten Less

ACROSS		DOWN	
1)	10	2)	20
3)	80	4)	10
5)	15	6)	50
7)	25	8)	5
9)	90	10)	40
11)	100	12)	90

SKIPS CHALLENGE

A. Copy out the largest number: 2 0 0

B. Copy out the smallest number: 3 6

Page 22-23 Five More or Five Less

ACROSS		DOWN	
1)	15	2)	50
5)	45	3)	15
7)	50	4)	20
8)	5	6)	55
9)	9	10)	90
12)	100	11)	5

SKIPS CHALLENGE

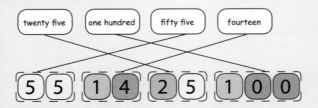

twenty five   one hundred   fifty five   fourteen

5 5   1 4   2 5   1 0 0

Page 24-25 Highest or Lowest?

ACROSS		DOWN	
1)	14	2)	20
3)	25	5)	32
4)	10	6)	29
9)	9	7)	5
11)	8	8)	16
12)	17	10)	7

SKIPS CHALLENGE

A. 2 + 1 0 + 3 = 1 5

B. 1 9 − 5 − 1 = 1 3

Page 26-27 How Much Money?

ACROSS		DOWN	
2)	15	1)	25
4)	25	3)	17
5)	2	7)	7
6)	27	8)	9
11)	21	9)	4
12)	4	10)	9

SKIPS CHALLENGE

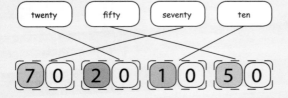

twenty   fifty   seventy   ten

7 0   2 0   1 0   5 0

Page 28-29 Odd and Even Numbers

ACROSS		DOWN	
1)	14	2)	10
3)	13	5)	21
4)	10	6)	13
10)	33	7)	26
11)	23	8)	11
12)	30	9)	20
13)	20		

SKIPS CHALLENGE

1 0   2 5   3 2   3 1   1 1

A. Copy out the smallest ODD number: 1 1

B. Copy out the largest ODD number: 3 1

Page 30-31 Number Sequences

ACROSS		DOWN	
1)	24	3)	18
2)	10	4)	22
6)	18	5)	29
8)	10	7)	20
9)	20	10)	11
11)	20		

SKIPS CHALLENGE

1 0   2 0   3 0   4 0   5 0

Page 32-33 What's the Time?

ACROSS		DOWN	
1)	8	2)	6
3)	3	5)	5
4)	10	7)	4
6)	2	8)	8
9)	11	10)	6
12)	10	11)	5

SKIPS CHALLENGE

A. 1 1 : 0 0 and 1 1 : 3 0

There are 3 0 minutes between these two times.

B. 1 1 : 0 0 and 1 2 : 0 0

There are 6 0 minutes between these two times.

For more SKIPS titles visit our website.

Page 34-35 Chapter Two – Test

ACROSS		DOWN	
1)	32	3)	26
2)	10	4)	17
5)	10	6)	25
7)	27	8)	5
11)	20	9)	7
12)	28	10)	40

SKIPS CHALLENGE

1 9 2 7 4 3 1 0

Copy out the EVEN number: 1 0

Page 36-37 CrossMaths Practice 1

ACROSS		DOWN	
1)	14	2)	10
3)	13	5)	21
4)	10	6)	13
10)	33	7)	26
11)	23	8)	11
12)	30	9)	20
13)	20		

SKIPS CHALLENGE

You have 2 5 p. You buy a drink for 1 0 p.

How much money do you have left? 1 5 p.

Page 38-39 CrossMaths Practice 2

ACROSS		DOWN	
1)	3	4)	7
2)	7	5)	3
3)	11	6)	9
8)	16	7)	17
11)	29	9)	22
12)	27	10)	27

SKIPS CHALLENGE

A. What is the difference between

1 7 and 1 3 ? 4

B. What is the number that comes between

1 0 and 1 2 ? 1 1

Page 40-41 CrossMaths Practice 3

ACROSS		DOWN	
1)	32	3)	26
2)	10	4)	17
5)	10	6)	25
7)	27	8)	5
11)	20	9)	7
12)	28	10)	40

SKIPS CHALLENGE

1 9 1 6 1 3 1 0 7

Page 42-43 CrossMaths Practice 4

ACROSS		DOWN	
1)	32	2)	25
4)	20	3)	20
8)	22	5)	29
9)	34	6)	30
10)	21	7)	32
12)	18	11)	27

SKIPS CHALLENGE

4 2 8 3

A. Using two of the boxes, what is the biggest
2 digit number you can make? 8 4

B. Using two of the boxes, what is the smallest
2 digit number you can make? 2 3

Page 44-45 CrossMaths Practice 5

ACROSS		DOWN	
1)	10	3)	30
2)	20	4)	15
5)	27	6)	20
7)	49	8)	13
9)	17	10)	11
12)	19	11)	22

SKIPS CHALLENGE

A cube has 6 faces,

1 2 edges

and 8 corners.

NOTES

For more SKIPS titles visit our website.

Hundred Square Help

Use this Hundred Square to help you to find an answer.

1	2	3	4	5	6	7	8	9	10
11	12	13	14	15	16	17	18	19	20
21	22	23	24	25	26	27	28	29	30
31	32	33	34	35	36	37	38	39	40
41	42	43	44	45	46	47	48	49	50
51	52	53	54	55	56	57	58	59	60
61	62	63	64	65	66	67	68	69	70
71	72	73	74	75	76	77	78	79	80
81	82	83	84	85	86	87	88	89	90
91	92	93	94	95	96	97	98	99	100

The Hundred Square can help us to find an answer

Hints

The Hundred Square can help us spot counting patterns or sequences and it can also be used for Adding and Taking Away. For example:

Go DOWN ↓ to find 10 more   Go RIGHT → to find 1 more

Go UP ↑ to find 10 less   Go LEFT ← to find 1 less

ORDER FORM

TITLE		RRP
SKIPS KS1 CrossWord Puzzles Key Stage 1 English	ISBN 978-0-9567526-5-9	£7.99
SKIPS KS1 CrossMaths Puzzles Key Stage 1 Maths	ISBN 978-0-9567526-4-2	£7.99
SKIPS KS2 CrossWord Puzzles Key Stage 2 English Book 1	ISBN 978-0-9567526-6-6	£7.99
SKIPS KS2 CrossWord Puzzles Key Stage 2 English Book 2	ISBN 978-0-9567526-2-8	£7.99
SKIPS KS2 CrossMaths Puzzles Key Stage 2 Maths Book 1	ISBN 978-0-9567526-7-3	£7.99
SKIPS KS2 CrossMaths Puzzles Key Stage 2 Maths Book 2	ISBN 978-0-9567526-3-5	£7.99
SKIPS 11+ CrossWord Puzzles 11 Plus English	ISBN 978-0-9567526-0-4	£9.99
SKIPS 11+ CrossMaths Puzzles 11 Plus Maths	ISBN 978-0-9567526-1-1	£9.99

Teachers and Tutors

You will be eligible for discounts on purchases of sets of 10 copies or more. Please get in touch for more details.

 sales@skipscrosswords.co.uk

 www.skipscrosswords.co.uk

 SKIPS Crosswords
142 Newton Road, Great Barr
Birmingham B43 6BT
UK